A Cat's Guide to Shakespeare

A CAT'S GUIDE TO SHAKESPEARE

Featuring Miracle and Magic

Gloria Luvina Johnson

Todd & Honeywell, Inc.

Copyright © 1987 by Gloria Luvina Johnson
First Edition

All rights reserved. No part of this publication may be reproduced or transmitted in any form or by any means, electronic or mechanical, including photocopy, recording or any information storage and retrieval system, without permission in writing from the publishers.

Published by Todd & Honeywell, Inc./Ten Cuttermill Road/ Great Neck, New York 11021

ISBN 0-89962-617-3

Manufactured in the United States of America

Dedication

To Carol, Deborah, Don, Edith, Dr. Han, Linda, Michelle, Roxanne, Dr. Tupper, Virginia

All the world's a stage,
And all the men and women
   merely players:
They have their exits and
   their entrances...

As You Like It

What do you read, my lord?
Words, words, words.

Hamlet, Prince of Denmark

...to sleep;
To sleep: perchance to dream...
Hamlet, Prince of Denmark

4

How now! a rat?

Hamlet, Prince of Denmark

For beauty, wit,
High birth, vigor of bone...

Troilus and Cressida

Doubt thou the stars are fire;
   Doubt that the sun doth move;
Doubt truth to be a liar;
   But never doubt I love.

Hamlet, Prince of Denmark

Now is the winter of our discontent
Made glorious...

King Richard the Third

Yond Cassius has a lean
and hungry look...

Julius Caesar

Out, damned spot! out, I say!
...all the perfumes of Arabia will
not sweeten this little hand.

Macbeth

I am, indeed, sir,
a surgeon to old shoes...

Julius Caesar

...to hold, as 'twere, the mirror
up to nature...

Hamlet, Prince of Denmark

But soft, what light through yonder
   window breaks?
It is the east, and Juliet is
   the sun.

Romeo and Juliet

For you and I are past our
 dancing days...

Romeo and Juliet

All orators are dumb when
 beauty pleadeth...

Lucrece

The lady protests too much, methinks.

Hamlet, Prince of Denmark

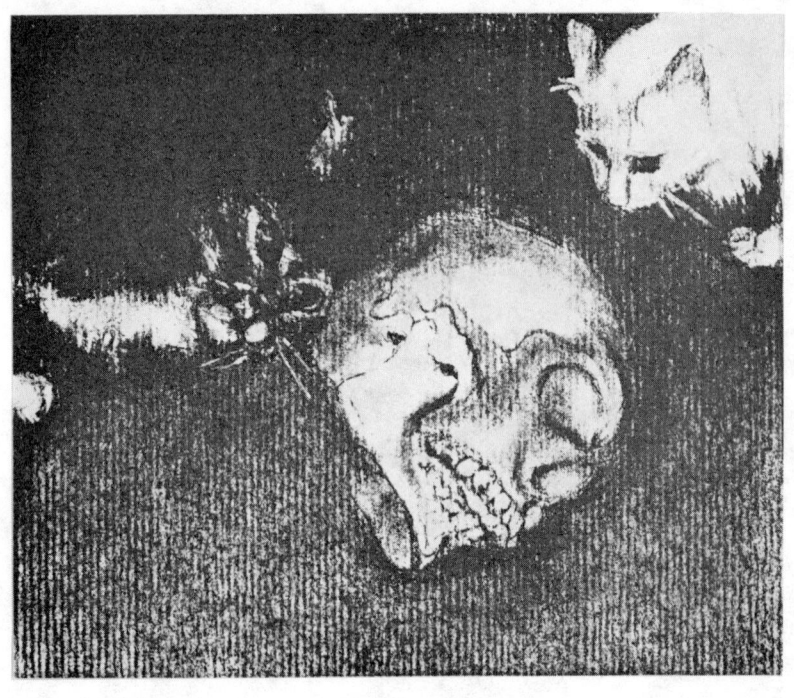

Alas, poor Yorick!
I knew him...

Hamlet, Prince of Denmark

She sat like patience on a monument...
Twelfth Night

What's to come is still unsure:
In delay, there lies no plenty;
Then come kiss me, sweet and twenty,
Youth's a stuff will not endure.

Twelfth Night

...honest water, which ne'er left man i' the mire...

Timon of Athens

Your mind is tossing on the ocean...
The Merchant of Venice

I do desire we may be better strangers.

As You Like It

This news is old enough,
yet it is every day's news.

Measure for Measure

Here will we sit and let the sounds
 of music
Creep in our ears: soft stillness and
 the night
Become the touches of sweet harmony.
The Merchant of Venice

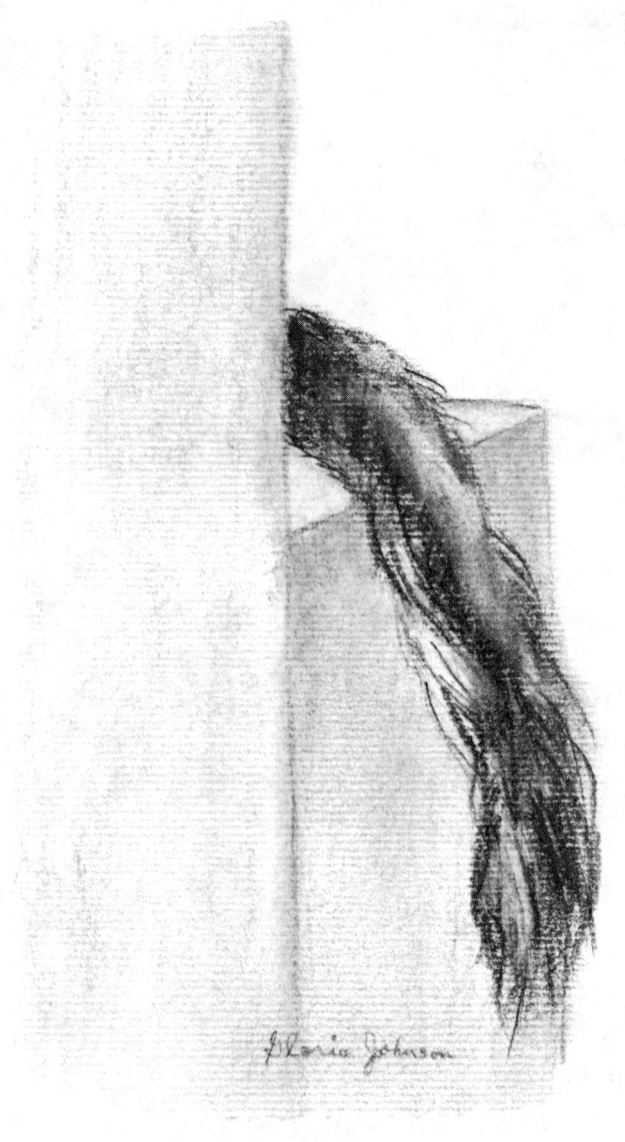

...and thereby hangs a tale.
The Taming of the Shrew

All's well that ends well...
All's Well That Ends Well